# Specials!

# World War 2

Susan Merritt

United Kingdom: Folens Publishers, Waterslade House, Thame Road, Haddenham, Buckinghamshire HP17 8NT.

Email: folens@folens.com

Ireland: Folens Publishers, Greenhills Road, Tallaght, Dublin 24.

Email: info@folens.ie

Editor: Janice Baiton          Layout artists: Book Matrix, India          Illustrations: Tony Randell

Cover design: Holbrook Design          Cover image: Corbis

First published 2007 by Folens Limited.

Every effort has been made to contact copyright holders of material used in this publication. If any copyright holder has been overlooked, we should be pleased to make any necessary arrangements.

British Library Cataloguing in Publication Data. A catalogue record for this publication is available from the British Library.

ISBN 978-1-85008-267-5

# Contents

# Introduction

*Specials! History* have been specifically written for teachers to use with students who may struggle with some of the skills and concepts needed for Key Stage 3 History. The titles are part of a wider series from Folens for use with lower ability students

Each book in the series contains ten separate units covering the topics needed to complete the theme of the book. Each unit has one or more photocopiable resource pages and several activity sheets. This allows the teacher to work in different ways. The tasks are differentiated throughout the book and offer all students the opportunity to expand their skills. By using photocopiable writing frames and emphasising literacy skills, students will be able to access historical information more easily.

The teacher's page at the start of each unit gives guidance on the material and is laid out as follows.

## Objectives

These are the main skills or knowledge to be learned.

## Prior knowledge

This refers to the minimum skills or knowledge required by students to complete the tasks. As a rule, students should have a reading comprehension age of 6 to 9 years and should be working at levels 1 to 3. Some activity sheets are more challenging than others and teachers will need to select accordingly.

## QCA and NC links; Scottish attainment targets; Northern Ireland links

All units link to the QCA Schemes of Work and to the NC for History at Key Stage 3. There are also links to the Scottish 5–14 guidelines and to the Northern Ireland NC.

## Background

This provides additional information for the teacher, expanding on historical details or giving further information about the unit.

## Starter activity

Since the units can be taught as a lesson, a warm-up activity focusing on an aspect of the unit is suggested.

## Resource and activity sheets

The resource sheets, which are often visual but may also be written, do not include tasks and can be used as stimulus for discussion. Related tasks are provided on the activity sheets.

Where necessary, keywords are included on the student pages. Other keywords are included on the teacher's page. These can be introduced to students at the teacher's discretion and depending on students' abilities.

## Assessment sheet

At the end of the book is an assessment sheet focusing on student progress. It can be used in different ways. A student can complete it as a self-assessment, while the teacher also completes one on each student's progress. They can then compare the two. This is useful in situations where the teacher or classroom assistant is working with one student. Alternatively, students can work in pairs to carry out peer assessments and then compare the outcomes with each other. Starting from a simple base that students can manage, the assessment sheet allows the student to discuss their own progress, to consider different points of view and to discuss how they might improve, thus enabling the teacher to see the work from the student's perspective.

## Plenary

The teacher can use the suggestions here to recap on the main points covered or to reinforce a particular idea.

Look out for other titles in the *History* series, which include:

- The Romans
- Medieval Britain 1066–1485
- Changing Britain 1485–1750
- Industrial Britain 1750–1900
- Britain in the 20th century

- The Holocaust
- Black peoples of the Americas
- Women and the vote
- World War 1
- The French Revolution

# Teacher's notes

## How did Hitler come to power?

### Objectives

- Understand that Europe was in depression after World War 1
- Be able to give reasons why there was depression in Europe
- Investigate the ways in which Hitler tried to appeal to different aspects of society

### Prior knowledge

Students should know that the Treaty of Versailles (1919) was supposed to prevent a world war from happening again, and that it was unpopular with the German people.

### QCA link

*Unit 18* Twentieth-century conflicts

### NC Links

History skills 2a, 2b, 3a, 3b

### Scottish attainment targets

*Environmental Studies – Social Subjects – People in the Past*
Strand – People, events and societies of significance in the past
Level D
*Environmental Studies – Skills in Social Subjects – Enquiry*
Strand – Reviewing and reporting on tasks
Level D

### Northern Ireland NC links

Study unit 4, The Twentieth Century World
b) a major event or person, e.g. the rise of Dictators (Hitler)

## Background

When World War 1 ended, the map and culture of the old Europe ended with it. Many of the old empires fell. The Austro-Hungarian Empire and the Russian Empire collapsed when their monarchies were replaced. Germany lost most of its empire, army and navy and many important industrial areas under the terms of the Treaty of Versailles. It was also forced, on paper at least, to pay massive reparations to other countries as a punishment for 'causing' the war. France and Britain thought that this arrangement was fair because the huge cost of the war had left them in a state of economic depression, and they still had to rebuild their industry, and in the case of France, much of their country. However, this state of affairs greatly angered the Germans, who were also in the midst of chaotic restructuring and depression. The unstable and indecisive Weimar Republic exacerbated German frustrations. This led to radical political parties flourishing as the German people became desperate for an end to their misery.

### Starter activity

Discuss the question 'How did World War 1 end?' and write the students' comments on the board. Ask the students how they would punish Germany.

### Resource sheets and activity sheets

Read and discuss 'Blame World War 1!' as a class.

'Europe after World War 1' gives students the opportunity to consolidate the information from 'Blame World War 1!' and put it into their own words.

'Crisis in Germany!' and then 'Hope and Hitler' guide students through the events that led to Hitler gaining political power in the Reichstag and will also give them an insight into how Hitler was able to manipulate public opinion for his own ends. They are given the opportunity to write a short election speech for Hitler that outlines his promises and appeal.

'Hail Hitler!' shows how Hitler manipulated both the public and the government to gain total power in Germany. Students are given the opportunity to create their own piece of Nazi propaganda so they can better understand how he appealed to small sections of the public.

### Plenary

Invite students to show their propaganda posters and give a prize for the most manipulative or creative piece.

# Blame World War 1!

Many historians argue that World War 1 caused World War 2. That might sound a bit strange as World War 2 happened in 1939, which was 21 years after World War 1 ended, but there are some very good reasons why there is some truth to that argument.

**1  The Treaty of Versailles**

At the end of World War 1, a **treaty** was signed to secure peace. This Treaty of Versailles was supposed to stop another world war from ever happening again. Some countries, such as Britain and France, wanted to punish Germany for its involvement in the war and they wanted to blame Germany for what happened. As a result, the Treaty of Versailles was very harsh on Germany.

**The Treaty of Versailles**

1  Germany is to blame for the war.
2  Germany must give all of its colonies to Britain and France.
3  Germany must get rid of most of its army and weapons.
4  Germany must pay millions of pounds, mainly to France but also to Britain and its allies.

**2  Poverty in Europe**

World War 1 cost a lot of money. All the countries that were involved in the war were in **debt** by the end of the war. They also had to rebuild their **industry** and **agriculture** because they had put more effort and money into building weapons for the war than growing food or making goods to sell. When World War 1 finally ended, the countries of Europe were too poor to do this, so many people were unemployed and hungry.

**3  Political chaos**

At the end of World War 1, many of the old **governments** of Europe collapsed. This means that some countries, such as Germany, Austria, Russia and Italy, had to have completely new governments. These were often inexperienced and made some mistakes. Some people did not trust their new governments and many countries had several **elections** that led to even more change.

# Activity sheet – How did Hitler come to power?

# Europe after World War 1

☞ Use the information on resource sheet 'Blame World War 1' to help you to answer the questions below about the problems in Europe after 1918.

| Why was Europe so poor after World War 1? | How do you think the political problems made the situation worse? |
|---|---|
| _____ | _____ |
| _____ | _____ |
| _____ | _____ |
| _____ | _____ |
| _____ | _____ |
| _____ | _____ |

## Problems caused by World War 1

Can you think of any reasons why the Treaty of Versailles would make Germany angry?

_____

_____

_____

_____

_____

_____

_____

_____

☞ Discuss with a partner ways that you think Europe could solve all these problems.

# Crisis in Germany!

After World War 1 finished, a new **democratic** government came to power in Germany. Democratic means that the people of Germany voted it in. It was called the **Weimar Republic**. It had a very difficult job to do. Germany was in a bad state after the war. **Unemployment** was very high because German industry had been used to build weapons for the war. Now the war was over, there was no need to make weapons. The lack of jobs meant that the people earned no wages so they were very poor.

To make matters worse for the Weimar Republic, one of the first things they did was to sign the Treaty of Versailles. They were forced to do this by Britain, France and the United States. This did not make the new government look good to the German people. They felt the Weimar Republic had betrayed them!

**Reparations**

The Treaty of Versailles forced Germany to pay enormous **reparations**. This was like a fine for doing something wrong. Germany was already poor, so the reparations made it worse. To make their money go further, the Weimar Republic printed more money. This had a very bad effect as it made prices go up because the money was now worth less. This is called **inflation**. Inflation got so bad in Germany that it took a wheelbarrow full of money to buy just one loaf of bread! The businesses and industries that had survived the war started to close and poverty became worse. The German people now wanted the Weimar Republic to go!

# Hope and Hitler

While the Weimar Republic tried to find a way of fixing all Germany's problems, a new politician came on the scene. His name was Adolf Hitler. Hitler had some very extreme political ideas, but he was a very clever man and a very good public speaker. He travelled around Germany and gave speeches to the people. He said that the Weimar Republic needed to go because they had made the mess that Germany was in. He called them **traitors** for signing the Treaty of Versailles and agreeing to pay Germany's enemies **reparations**. Hitler called the Treaty a 'stab in the back' as it was so unfair to Germany.

He promised the German people that if they voted for him, he would get rid of the Treaty and end reparations. This made him very popular with the German public. He made different promises to different types of people. For example, he promised the unemployed new jobs, and the starving bread. More and more people began to think that Adolf Hitler and his Nazi Party should run the German government. During 1930 and 1932, the **Nazi** Party began to win many seats in the German parliament, which was called the **Reichstag**.

☞ Imagine that Hitler is giving a speech to the poor unemployed people in a German town in 1932. What sort of things would he say to convince them to vote for him?

Good people of Germany

_____

_____

_____

_____

_____

_____

_____

_____

_____

World War 2

# Activity sheet – How did Hitler come to power?

# Hail Hitler!

In 1933, Hitler had enough seats in the **Reichstag** to be made **Chancellor** of Germany. He was in charge of the government, but he still had to listen to what the Reichstag said. Hitler wanted even more power and he knew that the best way to get it would be to convince the public that the other political parties were not any good.

One night in 1933, there was a mysterious fire at the Reichstag building. Hitler blamed the **Communist Party** for the fire and said that they had done it on purpose. People now think that it was Hitler who had arranged for the fire. However, the Communists were unpopular with many of the people at the Reichstag, so Hitler's story was believed. To help calm things down, Hitler was given more power. This made him a **Dictator**. This meant that he could do as he wanted. One of the first things he did was to ban all other political parties, so nobody could challenge him in an election! Many of Hitler's enemies began to disappear and soon people became too scared to stand up to him. He started to do things that most Germans felt were too extreme before, such as trying to force the **Jews** to leave Germany.

☞ In the boxes below are some of Hitler's ideas for the future of Germany. Choose one of them. On a separate piece of paper, create a propaganda poster advertising the benefits of this to the German people.

---

Hitler believed that all boys should be trained as good Nazi soldiers. He set up a group called the **Hitler Youth** to train them. The boys wore a brown uniform and practised marching and obeying orders. After a while, this was made **compulsory**.

---

Hitler believed that he could create a **master race** of German-speaking people who would take over the world. A perfect German would be an **Aryan**. This means that they would have blonde hair, blue eyes and believe in **Nazi** ideas.

---

Hitler thought that anyone who did not believe in his ideas was his enemy. He had a secret police force called the **Gestapo** that would capture and get rid of his enemies. He convinced people to give the Gestapo the names of all non-Nazis.

# Teacher's notes

## How did World War 2 start?

### Objectives

- Understand why Europe was reluctant to have another war
- Understand the events that led to the war starting
- Create a short written piece
- Organise a series of dates in chronological order

### Prior knowledge

Students should have some understanding of the radical beliefs of Hitler and know that he wanted more land for Germany.

### QCA link

*Unit 18* Twentieth-century conflicts

### NC links

History skills 1a, 2c, 5b, 5c

### Scottish attainment targets

*Environmental Studies – Social Subjects – People in the Past*
Strand – People, events and societies of significance in the past
*Level D*
Strand – Time and historical sequence
*Level C*

### Northern Ireland NC links

Study unit 4, The Twentieth Century World: Pearl Harbor, the D-Day Landings
a) the impact of World War: the invasion of Poland

## Background

When Hitler assumed the powers of Dictator in Germany, he began to systematically break many of the terms of the Treaty of Versailles. He stopped making reparation payments, began to re-arm in earnest and made plans for his belief in the Third Reich.

One of Hitler's most ardent beliefs was that all German-speaking peoples should be united as part of a new German Empire. He also believed in *Lebensraum* or 'living space' for the expanding German population.

In other words, for Germany to become great again, it needed to expand its territory into neighbouring countries to make room for his planned Nazi population boom.

In order to make these dreams a reality, Hitler needed to reclaim the important industrial areas lost in the Treaty of Versailles.

### Starter activity

Put the following keywords on the board and ask the students to write a definition of each of these in their books: *unemployment, reparations, inflation, dictator, propaganda.*

### Resource sheet and activity sheets

Begin by presenting the students with 'Invasions and annexations'. Read and discuss the text as a class. This will enable students to see that Hitler's expansion over Europe was a gradual, but decisive process.

'Poland – the final straw' gives students the opportunity to create a short written newspaper article to explain the chain of events that led to the outbreak of World War 2. Encourage the students to imagine that it is their job to describe how Hitler's actions led to war, so they need to explain why the invasion of Poland is so important.

'What happened during World War 2? (1)' and '(2)' provide a card sorting activity for students to practise their chronological skills. Students should cut out the cards and arrange the key events of World War 2 in chronological order. The cards could then be glued onto paper, or into exercise books, to create a timeline of the war for future reference.

### Plenary

Using the information from the timeline activity, have a quick-fire quiz in which students give the dates for a particular event or identify a event from a particular date.

# Invasions and annexations

Hitler believed that Germany should be bigger. He wanted all the people of Europe who spoke German to be part of Germany. Many of the countries of Europe, such as Austria, Czechoslovakia and Poland, had lots of German-speaking people living in them. Hitler wanted to add the land of these countries to Germany. He wanted to call this new giant Germany the **Third Reich**. However, the Treaty of Versailles prevented this.

Hitler broke the terms of the Treaty. He recruited a huge army in secret and made more weapons. In 1936, his army **invaded** the Rhineland. He waited to see what the other countries of Europe would do. They did nothing to stop him! In March 1938, his soldiers marched into Austria. He announced that Germany would **annex** Austria. This means that Austria would become part of Germany. Again, Europe did nothing to stop him. In September 1938, Hitler invaded part of Czechoslovakia, known as Sudetenland.

The **Prime Minister** of Britain, Neville Chamberlain, wanted to keep the peace in Europe. This policy was called **appeasement**. He signed a treaty called the **Munich Agreement** with Hitler. It said that Hitler could keep all the land he had taken, so long as he did not try to take any more. Chamberlain hoped that this would prevent war.

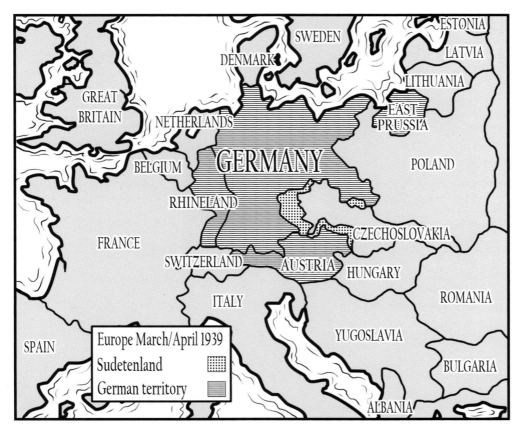

* The Sudetenland was an area that had been given to Czechoslovakia by the Treaty of Versailles. Many of the people that lived there spoke German.

World War 2

# Poland – the final straw

Hitler knew Europe did not want another war, so he ignored the **Munich Agreement**. In March 1939, he invaded the rest of Czechoslovakia. The governments of Europe started to worry that Hitler would take over if they did not stop him. In September 1939, Hitler invaded Poland. He believed he would be allowed to get away with it again. But on 3 September 1939, Britain and France declared war on Germany. World War 2 had begun.

☞ Use the template below to create a newspaper front page about the start of the war. Include the reasons why the war has started and Europe's fears about Adolf Hitler. Discuss ideas and key words with a partner first. There is also a space for a small picture to illustrate your story.

# We Are At War Again!

# What happened during World War 2? (1)

It would be very easy to blame Hitler for all that happened during World War 2, but that would not be fair. As in all wars, things got a bit confusing, and other countries joined in the fighting. In fact, it almost seemed as though there were two separate wars being fought at the same time – the war in Europe and the war in the Pacific.

☞ Each card below and on 'What happened during World War 2? (2)' tells you about different events and battles that took place during World War 2. Cut out all the cards and arrange them in chronological order to create a timeline of World War 2.

| | | |
|---|---|---|
| 24 May 1940<br>The evacuation of **Dunkirk** begins. Thousands of small boats sail from Britain to rescue the British soldiers trapped there. | 7 December 1941<br>The Japanese attack the United States base at **Pearl Harbor** in Hawaii. The USA joins the war as Britain's most powerful ally. | 6 June 1944<br>D-Day. The allied troops launch a surprise attack on the Nazis by landing thousands of troops on the beaches of Normandy. |
| September 1940<br>The **Battle of Britain** is a huge British success. Churchill thanks '**the Few**' for their bravery in stopping Hitler invading Britain. | 3 September 1939<br>Britain and France declare war on Germany. World War 2 had begun. | 30 April 1945<br>As the allies march towards Berlin, Hitler commits **suicide** in a secret underground bunker. |
| 1 September 1939<br>Hitler's army invades Poland. Soon Poland falls to the German army. | June 1944<br>After a long struggle, the USSR finally push the Nazis back. From now on, the army of the USSR will march forward and attack the Nazis. | May 1940<br>Hitler begins his **Blitzkrieg**. This means that he attacks Britain using the **Luftwaffe** as well as his army and navy. |

# What happened during World War 2? (2)

| | | |
|---|---|---|
| **7 September 1940** After failing to win the **Battle of Britain**, Hitler starts a huge bombing campaign against British towns and cities. It was called the **Blitz**. | **April 1940** The Nazis invade Norway and Denmark. They start to invade France. | **7 May 1945** Germany finally **surrenders**. The European war is over. Britain celebrates VE (Victory in Europe) Day on 8 May. |
| **August 1944** Allied troops **liberate** Paris. They start to march towards Germany. | **June 1941** Hitler starts **Operation Barbarossa**. This was his plan to invade the USSR quickly. However, his plan fails because of bad Russian weather. | **May 1943** The '**Desert Rats**' help push the Nazis out of Africa. The war is now going very badly for Hitler. |
| **22 June 1940** France officially **surrenders** to the Germans. | **6 August 1945** The USA drops the first **atomic bomb** on **Hiroshima**, Japan. A second bomb is dropped on **Nagasaki** three days later. Over 100 000 people killed. | **May 1940** **Winston Churchill** becomes the new Prime Minister of Britain after Chamberlain resigns. He warns Hitler that Britain 'shall never surrender'. |
| **14 August 1945** Japan **surrenders**. The war in the **Pacific** is now over and **VJ Day** (Victory in Japan Day) is celebrated. | **July 1940** The **Battle of Britain** begins. The **Royal Air Force** fights the **Luftwaffe** over Britain and the English Channel. | **May 1943** The **Dambusters** destroy a huge dam in the Ruhr using a new '**bouncing**' **bomb**. Many important German factories are flooded. |

# Teacher's notes

## What was the Home Front?

### Objectives

- Understand how the people at home helped the war effort
- Be able to extract information from sources

### Prior Knowledge

Students should understand that although the war was being fought abroad, it had an impact on life at home.

### QCA link

*Unit 18* Twentieth-century conflicts

### NC links

History skills 2b, 2c, 2e, 4a, 4b

### Scottish Attainment targets

*Environmental Studies – Social Subjects – People in the Past*
Strand – Change, continuity, cause and effect
Level D
Strand – People, events and societies of significance in the past
Level D

### Northern Ireland NC links

Study unit 4, The Twentieth Century World
a) the impact of World War

## Background

When the war broke out and conscription started, men were taken out of many vitally important jobs. As they had in World War 1, the government began to actively encourage women to fill the void in the labour market. Women began to take on roles that had previously been considered male occupations, such as fire fighters and even road diggers. Many women joined the armed forces where they performed the more mundane day-to-day duties to keep these services running effectively. For example, although they were never used in battle, female pilots ferried planes and supplies around Europe to free up the male pilots for combat. Similarly, older men, or those unable to fight, were encouraged to 'do their bit' and join some form of organised work to help the war effort.

### Starter activity

Ask the class to make a list of the jobs that they feel women would have been doing before the war broke out. These ideas can then be shared with the class.

### Resource sheet and activity sheets

Working either in groups or pairs, students should try to extract information from the posters in 'Women and the war' and 'The men left behind' to explain what the Women's Land Army and the Home Guard did. Encourage the students to look at the message in the posters. How is the government trying to get older men or women to recruit for these jobs?

'The Home Front' provides a more detailed explanation of the jobs people did to aid the war effort. This could be used for a discussion about how hard people worked during the war and what they had to give up in order to do their 'duty'. Students could then use this information to create a leaflet designed to encourage the public to do their duty. The leaflet should give details of the kind of work that was necessary and should try to make these jobs appealing to women and older men.

'Home Front mix and match' ensures that the students have understood all the information from this unit and also provides an opportunity to practise some literacy and decision-making skills. Each student will need a copy of the sheet, scissors and glue. On one half of the sheet are the sentence starters that students should match to the correct sentence endings. The completed sentences should be glued into their exercise books.

### Plenary

Play Home Front charades. Give a student a particular job from the Home Front, such as air raid warden, and ask the student to act this out for the class to guess.

# Women and the war

☞ 1  In groups or pairs, discuss the following questions:

a)  What is this government poster trying to say?

b)  What do you think the Women's Land Army did?

2  On a separate piece of paper, design a poster that encourages women to go to work to help the war effort.

# The men left behind

☞ 1    In groups or pairs, discuss the following questions:

   a)    What is this government poster trying to say?

   b)    What do you think the Home Guard did?

2    Imagine you are an older man during World War 2. On a separate piece of paper, write a diary extract explaining why you believe it is important for everybody to do their duty and help during the war.

# The Home Front

The term **Home Front** is used to describe all the things that the people at home did to help the **war effort**. With so many men away fighting, there was a shortage of people to do essential jobs, such as fire fighting or farming. Just as they had in World War 1, the government encouraged women to work in the jobs that had traditionally been done by men. Women made weapons in factories and became fire fighters and ambulance drivers. The **Women's Land Army** was introduced to supply labour to the many farms in Britain, so women ploughed fields and milked cows to help the war effort.

The men that were considered too old to fight in the armed forces were also encouraged to do other jobs to help the war effort. The **Home Guard** was set up to protect Britain from invasion. These soldiers were made up of older men who only wore the uniform part-time, as they all still had to do their normal work as well as their war work. Some older men took on extra responsibilities as **air-raid wardens** and checked that people were safe during a bombing raid. Others took jobs as **blackout wardens** or part-time firemen. This work was seen as important and showed everyone that you were prepared to do your duty even if you could not fight.

# Home Front mix and match

 Use your knowledge of the Home Front to complete the following sentences. In column A is a selection of sentence starters. In column B are the sentence endings. Each starter has only one correct ending. Cut out each beginning and ending and match them correctly. Then stick them into your book. Can you match them all correctly?

## Column A

The Women's Land Army sent young women

The government encouraged women and older men

An air-raid warden used

Older men took on extra jobs

A blackout warden used

The Home Guard used

Women took on jobs

## Column B

to check that people were safe during an air raid and would sound the alarm if any planes were spotted.

to patrol areas, such as beaches, to protect Britain from invasion.

to the countryside to work on farms because there was a shortage of men to do the work.

such as fire fighters, ambulance drivers, factory workers or they joined the Land Army.

to do their duty and take on a job that would help the war effort.

such as air raid wardens, blackout wardens or they joined the Home Guard.

to patrol the streets to see if any lights were visible in the dark.

# Teacher's notes

## What was life like at home?

### Objectives

- Compare the amount of food consumed during World War 2 with today
- Understand how propaganda was used to help rationing
- Research the ways in which rationing affected fashion
- Understand why children were evacuated

### Prior knowledge

Students should know that normal life was interrupted for many British people by the onset of the war.

### QCA link

*Unit 18* Twentieth-century conflicts

### NC links

History skills 2e, 4a, 4b, 5c, 7a

### Scottish attainment targets

*Environmental Studies – Social Subjects – People in the Past*
Strand – Change, continuity, cause and effect
Level D
Strand – People, events and societies of significance in the past
Level D

### Northern Ireland NC links

Study unit 4, The Twentieth Century World
a) the impact of World War

## Background

Almost as soon as World War 2 broke out, life for the civilians in Britain changed dramatically. The British reliance on foreign imports to make up for the agricultural shortfalls created an enormous problem. Rationing was introduced because the government feared that there was a very real danger of starvation in Britain unless the food was shared equally and monitored effectively. This problem was recognised and exploited by the Nazis, who made an effort to destroy

many of the ships that supplied Britain with staples. Campaigns such as 'Dig For Victory' and 'Make Do And Mend' did help, and made the British public feel much better about being deprived of many luxuries. Aside from rationing, the government also believed that the future generation should be protected from the war and so it actively encouraged the evacuation of children and babies from the cities and towns. Thousands were evacuated in 1939, but as this period of the war earned the nickname the 'phoney war', because of the lack of obvious fighting and danger to the mainland, many evacuees soon returned home. Many were evacuated again during the Blitz and remained away from their homes until the end of the war in 1945.

### Starter activity

Put the word *rationing* on the board. Ask students to make as many words (of at least two letters) as possible out of the letters. Students can only use each letter once in each word. Award a prize for the student who can make the most words.

### Resource sheet and activity sheets

Read and discuss 'Restrictions and rationing' as a class. Students should then complete the consolidation tasks.

'Dig For Victory' discusses the campaign to encourage people to grow their own food. Students should create their own poster for the Ministry of Food.

'Make Do And Mend!' gives the students an opportunity to use the Internet or library for independent research. It also gives kinaesthetic learners an opportunity to create a collage based on their research.

'Evacuees' tells the story of the many children who were sent away from home during the war.

'Evacuation diary' gives students the opportunity to empathise with the plight of the evacuees. After reading this sheet, the class could engage in a discussion about the experiences of evacuees.

### Plenary

Choose students at random to read out their diaries. Ask the rest of the class to peer assess the work by each giving one positive comment about the piece and a target or improvement.

# Restrictions and rationing

When the war broke out, Great Britain had a big problem – food! Since the **Industrial Revolution**, Britain had changed and its **agriculture** had become smaller. Even though farming had improved a great deal, Great Britain did not grow enough food to feed its entire **population**. Instead, a lot of food was **imported** from other countries and was sent to Britain in ships. However, as the war at sea got worse, it became more difficult for the food ships to get to Britain and many of them were sunk. The government had to do something to stop the population starving to death!

The **Ministry of Food** was set up to deal with this problem. It knew that the food would not run out if it could be shared out equally to everyone, so **rationing** was introduced. **Rationing** meant that each person would be issued with a **ration book**. Inside this book were **coupons** for different items that were in short supply. These coupons gave each person the right to buy a certain amount of each product each week. If you did not have the coupons for something in your ration book, you would not be allowed to buy it.

The picture below shows the weekly rations given to an adult during World War 2.

1 egg      50g tea (about 15 tea bags!)      1.8 litres milk      50g cheese

4 rashers of bacon      Meat worth 1 shilling      50g butter (about 4 teaspoons full!)

 1    On a separate sheet of paper, make a list of all the foods that you have eaten in the last five days. You must include all drinks except water.

    2    Estimate how much meat, cheese, eggs and milk have gone into all the foods on your list.

    3    Now compare the amounts on your list to the amounts allocated to the average adult given above. How much more of these foods do you eat? Could you survive on World War 2 rations?

# Dig For Victory!

Not all foods were rationed. Flour, bread and vegetables could be bought without coupons. However, the Ministry of Food tried to encourage people to grow as much of their own food as possible. They launched the **Dig For Victory** campaign. This was very successful as it convinced many people to stop growing flowers in their gardens and to plant vegetables instead. This poster is based on one of the most famous from the Dig For Victory campaign.

☞ You have been asked by the Ministry of Food to design a poster for the 'Dig For Victory' campaign to encourage people to grow their own potatoes. On a separate piece of paper, create a new poster and remember to include a new slogan.

# Make Do And Mend!

It was not only food that was rationed during the war. Petrol, coal and clothes were also rationed. The government started the **Make Do And Mend** campaign to encourage people to re-use old clothes and fabric. Dresses would be cut down to make skirts or children's clothes, woollen clothes would be unravelled and the wool would be knitted into something else. People would use all sorts of fabric to make things. For example, some wedding dresses were made from enemy parachute material!

 Research the types of clothing worn by people in World War 2. Look closely at the different styles and also at the types of colours that were used because of rationing. Use the template doll below and create accurate clothes for it using coloured paper and glue. Your doll can be male or female, just choose one of the two faces below, cut it out and stick it to your doll.

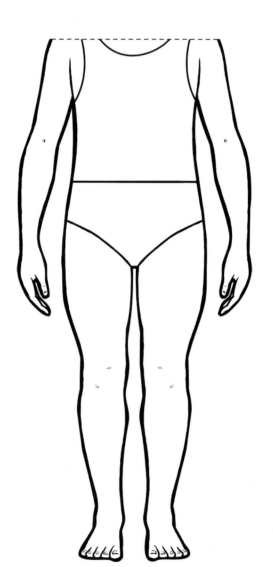

World War 2

# Evacuees

In the autumn of 1939, the government was afraid that many of the cities of Britain would be bombed. They decided that it would be safer for all the children in these cities to be moved to the countryside. They decided to **evacuate** the children of the large towns and cities to the country straight away. The government encouraged parents to evacuate their children to keep them out of danger. Thousands of **evacuees** were put on trains to the countryside. They did not know where they would be staying or who would be looking after them.

This must have been a very traumatic time for the children and their parents, as they did not know how long they would be separated for or if they would ever see each other again. The evacuees were allowed to take one small suitcase with them on their journey. When they arrived in the countryside, local families looked after them. Some evacuees were very lucky. They went to good homes and had a very pleasant time in the countryside, doing things that they would never have been able to do in the cities. For others, their evacuation stories are very different. Some of the people that took them in saw it as an ideal opportunity to get cheap labour on their farms and made the children work very hard. Others were cruel and beat the children in their care. Some evacuees were sent abroad to Canada, lost contact with their families and never returned.

# Activity sheet – What was life like at home?

# Evacuation diary

☞ You are a small child who is about to be evacuated during World War 2. Use the following template to write a diary extract about how you feel. You might like to include the following:

- Why you are being evacuated.
- What you are most afraid of.
- What you are looking forward to.

Dear diary,
Today I am being evacuated.

_____

_____

_____

_____

_____

_____

_____

_____

_____

☞ All evacuees are allowed to take one small suitcase with them. After you have packed your clothes, there is room left in your suitcase to take five items with you to remind you of home. On a separate piece of paper, write down the five items you are going to take and explain why you have chosen them.

# Teacher's notes

## What was the Battle of Britain?

### Objectives

- Understand what the Battle of Britain was
- Investigate one of the key battles of the war
- Communicate understanding by creating a storyboard

### Prior knowledge

Students should know that there were many important battles and turning points in World War 2.

### QCA link

*Unit 18* Twentieth-century conflicts

### NC links

History skills 3a, 5b, 5c, 7a

### Scottish attainment targets

*Environmental Studies – Social Subjects – People in the Past*
Strand – Change, continuity, cause and effect
Level E
*Environmental Studies – Social Subjects – People in the Past*
Strand – People, events and societies of significance in the past
Level E

### Northern Ireland NC links

Study unit 4, The Twentieth Century World
a) the impact of World War

## Background

In 1940, there was a very real possibility that Britain could not only lose the war, but could also be invaded. Hitler had already taken over many European countries and with the fall of France and the embarrassing British retreat at Dunkirk, the situation was looking increasingly bleak.

After public and parliamentary pressure, Chamberlain resigned as Prime Minister and Winston Churchill took over the role. Churchill promised the British people victory eventually, but warned of blood, toil, sweat and tears on the way.

British fears of a Nazi invasion became chillingly real in the summer of 1940 when Hitler launched the first part of 'Operation Sealion', the code word for the invasion of Britain. Hitler's plan was to win air supremacy before launching a full-blown land invasion.

### Starter activity

Put the following anagrams on the board for students to unscramble.
IVANNOSI Answer = INVASION.
RETHIL Answer = HITLER
LETBAT Answer = BATTLE

### Resource sheets and activity sheet

'We will fight them in the air!' provides students with the necessary background information that led up to the Battle of Britain. It is important that the students understand that Hitler was winning the war at this point and that had he invaded Britain by sea, there is a very real possibility that it would have been successful. However, he chose to tackle the RAF first.

'The Few: an outline of the battle' gives students a brief outline of the key features of the battle, broken down into small, easy to understand chunks.

'The Battle of Britain' gives students the opportunity to recreate the battle in a film storyboard that clearly describes key parts to the Battle of Britain. Less able students could use the template provided. More able students would benefit from creating their own storyboard on a plain piece of paper and including their own written synopsis of the battle. This task could be expanded by using other information, from the Internet, books or films, so that students have a thorough knowledge of this important turning point of the war.

### Plenary

On small pieces of paper, ask each student to write one question about the Battle of Britain. They can then use these as a quiz for each other.

# We will fight them in the air!

During 1939 and 1940, Hitler was winning the war. He had successfully invaded and taken over many countries in Europe, including Poland, Czechoslovakia, Belgium, Holland and Norway. The British and French armies suffered a huge defeat in France in May 1940, and thousands of British soldiers had to be rescued from the beaches of **Dunkirk**. After this, France **surrendered** to the Germans in June 1940 and Hitler began to make plans to invade Britain. The British put barbed wire over all the beaches where they feared the Germans could land.

The British Prime Minister, Neville Chamberlain, resigned because he was constantly criticised by the public. The new Prime Minister, Winston Churchill, gave the British people a new hope and promised them that 'We shall fight on the seas and oceans, we shall fight … in the air, we shall defend our Island, whatever the cost may be, we shall fight on the beaches, we shall fight on the landing grounds, we shall fight in the fields and in the streets, we shall fight in the hills; we shall never surrender!'

In July 1940, the **Luftwaffe** began to attack the **Royal Air Force**. Hitler believed that the RAF needed to be destroyed before he could invade Britain. The RAF had other ideas. They decided to fight back. This was called the **Battle of Britain**.

# The Few: an outline of the battle

## 1) Operation Sealion

In the summer of 1940, Hitler made plans to invade Britain. He called this plan **Operation Sealion**. First, he wanted to control the air over Britain, and then he planned to invade using the army and navy. The Battle of Britain began on 10 July 1940 as the **Luftwaffe** started to attack British ships.

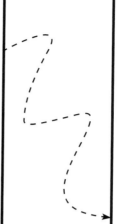

## 2) Eagle Day

On 13 August 1940, Hitler ordered a massive air attack against Britain. Hundreds of Luftwaffe planes were involved. However, Hitler underestimated the **RAF**, which shot down 45 Luftwaffe planes.

## 3) Attacking air bases

From the middle of August 1940, the Luftwaffe attacked the **RAF air bases**. This was a very good plan and the RAF suffered many losses. However, during this time, the RAF fought back. British pilots flew planes such as the **Spitfire** and the **Hurricane**. These small planes were much faster and easier to control than many of the German planes. As a result, many Luftwaffe planes were destroyed in the battle.

## 4) Changing tactics

On 7 September 1940, the Luftwaffe changed **tactics**. Instead of attacking the whole of Britain, they now directed all their attacks on London. They hoped that by attacking the capital city, they would win the battle. However, this proved to be a bad move for the Nazis, as the Luftwaffe had further to fly to get to London and could be easily surrounded by the RAF in their faster planes. After a week of heavy fighting, it soon became clear that the Luftwaffe could not beat the RAF. From here on, the Luftwaffe bombed British cities instead. The Battle of Britain had ended, but the **Blitz** had just begun!

# The Battle of Britain

☞ You would like to make a film about the Battle of Britain. Before the studio will agree to this, they insist that you provide them with a detailed storyboard of your ideas. Use the template below to create your storyboard.

| | |
|---|---|
| 1) Hitler plans to invade Great Britain. | 2) The Luftwaffe start to attack ships. |
| 3) The RAF Spitfires and Hurricanes fight the Luftwaffe over the Channel. | 4) The Luftwaffe begin to attack London. |
| 5) After days of severe fighting, the Luftwaffe realise that they cannot beat the RAF. Hitler's invasion plans are ruined. | |

# Teacher's notes

## What was the Blitz?

### Objectives

- Understand what happened in the Blitz
- Discover how people kept safe during an air raid
- Be familiar with and use the keywords
- Develop literary skills by producing a diary

### Prior knowledge

Students should know that Hitler was in an excellent strategic position in 1940, and that he was winning the war at this point.

### QCA link

*Unit 18* Twentieth-century conflicts

### NC links

History skills 5a, 5b, 6a

### Scottish attainment targets

*Environmental Studies – Social Subjects – People in the Past*
Strand – Nature of historical evidence
Level D
Strand – People, events and societies of significance in the past
Level D

### Northern Ireland NC links

Study unit 4, The Twentieth Century World
a) the impact of World War

## Background

After it became clear that Hitler and the Luftwaffe could not effectively win the Battle of Britain, they changed tactics. Instead of attacking the RAF head on, the Luftwaffe began a series of strategic bombing raids aimed at important British targets. Many cities, towns and ports were bombed from September 1940 using the Blitzkrieg tactics. These bombing raids were at their peak in 1940–41 and the British nicknamed this 'The Blitz'. London was hit the worst and the damage was huge, especially in the East End of the city. Despite this, Londoners were known to have tremendous resilience during this difficult time, although thousands of civilians were killed in the air raids and many buildings and streets totally destroyed.

### Starter activity

Ask the students to write the alphabet in a vertical column in their exercise books. Set a time limit and see how many World War 2 keywords they can find that begin with each letter. For example A = Air raid, B = Battle of Britain and so on. Award a prize for the student who gets the most.

### Resource sheets and activity sheets

Read and discuss 'Blitzkrieg!' and 'Seeking shelter' as a class.

For 'What should you do in an air raid?', students should create an information leaflet that explains survival techniques during the Blitz.

'Living in the Blitz' explains how the lives of ordinary British citizens were disrupted by the bombings and why blackouts and gas masks were compulsory.

'Surviving the Blitz: snakes and ladders (1)' and '(2)' provide a board game that gives students the opportunity to empathise with the plight of the civilians. The game boards can be enlarged on a photocopier so that a maximum of six students can play on each board. Students will need dice and coloured counters.

Students should record their Blitz 'experience' on the 'Blitz diary'. This could then lead to a discussion on the different experiences of the class. It could also be extended as a homework task by encouraging the students to interview older friends and relatives about their wartime experiences for comparison and further discussion.

### Plenary

Play keyword bingo. Put a selection of the keywords from this topic on the board. Give each student a blank bingo grid and ask them to select between four and six words (depending on time) to put in the grid. To play bingo, ask questions that have the keywords as the answers. If students have the correct keyword on their grid, they can cross it off. The winner is the first student to cross off all their chosen keywords.

# Blitzkrieg!

In the autumn of 1940, Hitler began using a new tactic to beat the British. He called it the **Blitzkrieg**. This literally means 'lightning war'. He used the **Luftwaffe** to bombard the important cities, ports and factories of Britain. The bombs were dropped on Britain starting on 7 September 1940. Hundreds of German planes flew over the cities and thousands of bombs were dropped. The British nicknamed these attacks the **Blitz**.

### Air raids, ack-acks and doodlebugs

The British people were warned of a bombing attack by the **air-raid sirens**. These would let out a loud, piercing noise that would sound for two minutes to signal that enemy planes had been spotted. This would tell people that they needed to find **shelter**. Most attacks happened during the night as it was easier for the enemy planes to hide in the dark and avoid the **anti-aircraft guns**.

The anti-aircraft guns, or **ack-acks** as they were nicknamed by the British public, were very powerful guns that could fire at a plane high above. At night, giant **searchlights** were used to find the planes in the dark.

Later in the war, the Germans used other types of bombs to attack British cities. One of these was the **V1 rocket**, which the British nicknamed the **doodlebug**. This was a special type of bomb that did not need a pilot. Instead, the rocket would fly over Britain until it ran out of fuel and then it would drop from the sky and explode.

The Luftwaffe

World War 2

# Seeking shelter

When the air-raid sirens warned of an attack, the British people ran for the nearest shelter. There were many different types of shelter that they could use. The most common one was called an **Anderson Shelter**. This was a small building, a bit like a shed, that could be built in people's back gardens. It was made of **corrugated iron** and most of the shelter had to be buried underground in a big hole and then the roof would be covered in mud.

Many people in London used the **Underground**, nicknamed the **Tube**, for shelter. At night, thousands would flock down to the tunnels of the Tube and sleep on the station **platforms**. Usually, the Tube was a very safe place during an air raid as the stations were built very deep under the ground. It was also one of the few places where the noise of the bombs could not be heard.

However, on a few rare occasions, the Tube was a dangerous place to be. In one tragic accident on 3 March 1943, 172 people were crushed to death as thousands rushed into Bethnal Green station during an air raid. Despite this, the Tube was the favourite choice of shelter for many Londoners and it gained a reputation for being a friendly and cheerful place to be at night.

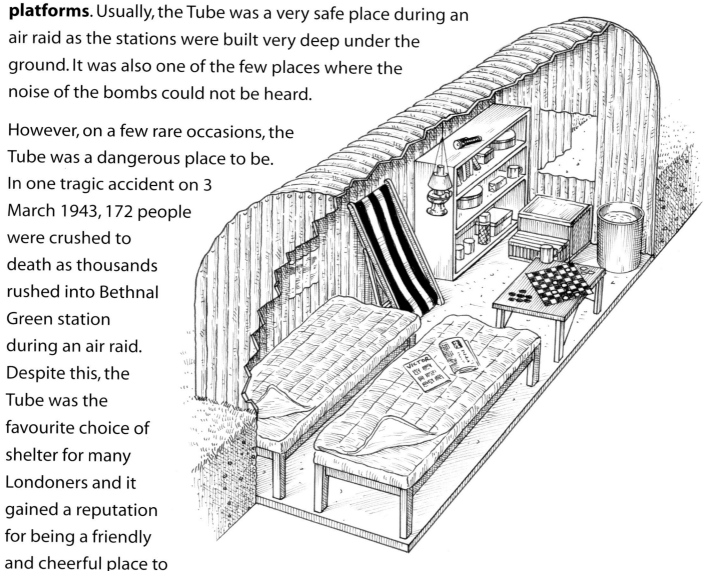

An Anderson shelter

World War 2

# What should you do in an air raid?

☞ Use the template below to create a leaflet telling the people of London what they need to do in an air raid. Your leaflet will need to include information about air-raid sirens, shelters and tips to help people to survive in a shelter for many hours.

*Staying safe during the Blitz!*

Tips to help you stay alive!

# Living in the Blitz

During World War 2, the public had to deal with many new things. As you have learned, food and clothing were rationed. There were also many new rules that had to be obeyed. One of these was that everybody had to carry a **gas mask** with them at all times. During World War 1, poisonous gas had been used as a weapon. The government feared that the Nazis would drop **gas bombs** on Britain.

To protect the public, everybody was issued with a gas mask. Even small children and babies had to have gas masks. If you were caught outside without your gas mask, you could be fined. Despite the government's fears, gas was never dropped onto Britain, so no member of the British public ever used their mask!

Another new rule that had to be obeyed was the **blackout**. This was a very sensible rule as the enemy aircraft used the lights of a city to identify where it was. Every night, as soon as it got dark, the public had to make sure that no lights from their houses could be seen from outside. Thick curtains had to be put up at every window and all street lamps were turned off. If you needed to be outside, you were allowed to use a torch to help you to see, but most of the beam had to be covered up with tape. You also had to cover up most of a car's headlamps as well. **Wardens** could fine people who broke the **blackout regulations**.

World War 2

# Surviving the Blitz: snakes and ladders (1)

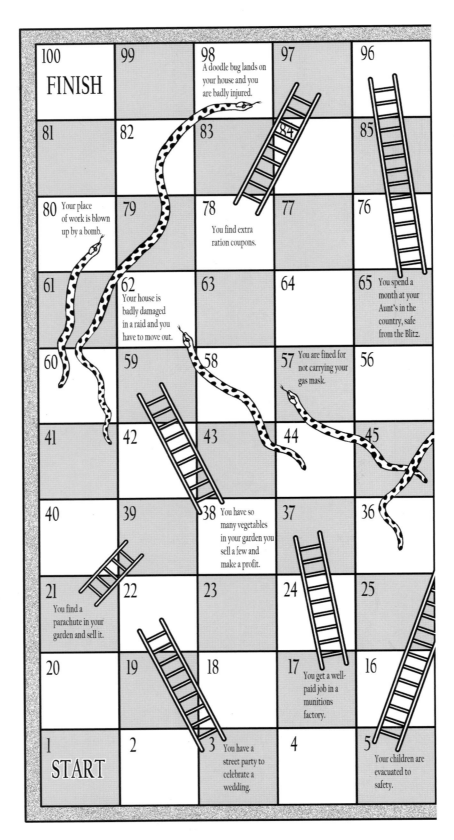

| | | | | |
|---|---|---|---|---|
| 100 FINISH | 99 | 98 A doodle bug lands on your house and you are badly injured. | 97 | 96 |
| 81 | 82 | 83 | 84 | 85 |
| 80 Your place of work is blown up by a bomb. | 79 | 78 You find extra ration coupons. | 77 | 76 |
| 61 | 62 Your house is badly damaged in a raid and you have to move out. | 63 | 64 | 65 You spend a month at your Aunt's in the country, safe from the Blitz. |
| 60 | 59 | 58 | 57 You are fined for not carrying your gas mask. | 56 |
| 41 | 42 | 43 | 44 | 45 |
| 40 | 39 | 38 You have so many vegetables in your garden you sell a few and make a profit. | 37 | 36 |
| 21 You find a parachute in your garden and sell it. | 22 | 23 | 24 | 25 |
| 20 | 19 | 18 | 17 You get a well-paid job in a munitions factory. | 16 |
| 1 START | 2 | 3 You have a street party to celebrate a wedding. | 4 | 5 Your children are evacuated to safety. |

# Surviving the Blitz: snakes and ladders (2)

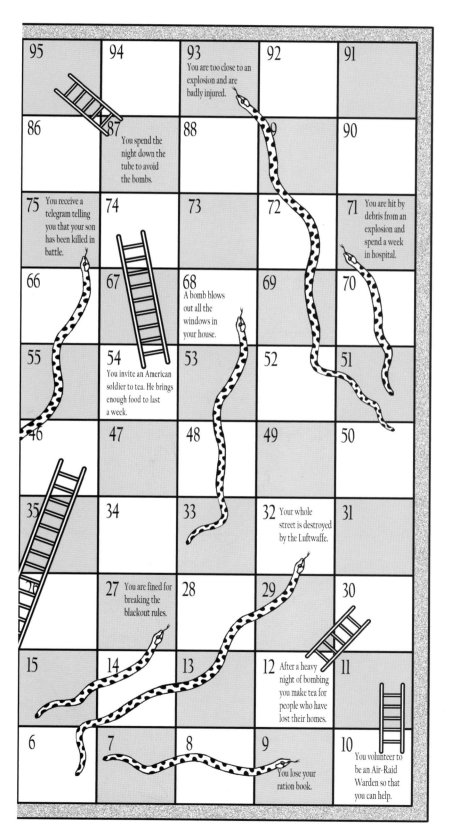

# Blitz diary

☞ Play the 'Snakes and ladders' game and use it to create a diary account of your experiences of the Blitz. Use the template below to help you. Record all the good things and bad things that happen to you while you play the game. Then use your diary to write a story that explains your experience of the Blitz.

| | What happened to you? | How would this make you feel? |
|---|---|---|
| 1 | | |
| 2 | | |
| 3 | | |
| 4 | | |
| 5 | | |
| 6 | | |
| 7 | | |
| 8 | | |
| 9 | | |
| 10 | | |

World War 2

# Teacher's notes

## How were secrets passed on?

### Objectives

- Understand that secrecy was very important during the war
- Understand how codes were used
- Be able to decipher and create simple codes

### Prior knowledge

Students should know that modern computers and calculators had not been invented during World War 2, so all problems had to be worked out by people.

### QCA link

*Unit 18* Twentieth-century conflicts

### NC links

History skills 2a, 5c

### Scottish attainment targets

*Environmental Studies – Technology – People in the Past*
Strand – People, events and societies of significance in the past
Level D
Strand – Change and continuity, cause and effect
Level E

### Northern Ireland NC links

Study unit 4, The Twentieth Century World
a) the impact of World War

## Background

For the first half of the war, the Nazis proved to be very good at preventing their enemies from deciphering the coded messages that were sent over the airwaves. This was largely because of the Enigma machine. The machine itself was technologically quite simple, using a basic keyboard and rotors. The message would be typed in letter by letter and the code would light up on a panel above the keyboard. The beauty of the machine was its ability to change the code regularly, using one of literally millions of different combinations. To decipher the code, you needed to have the code-book as well as another Enigma machine. The Nazis went to extraordinary lengths to prevent their enemies from getting their hands on these, even going as far as printing the code-books with a special ink that dissolved on contact with water so that they could be easily destroyed.

### Starter activity

Put the following code on the board and ask the students to solve it:
If A =1 and Z = 26, what does the following code say:
20,15,16   19,5,3,18,5,20
(Answer: TOP SECRET)

### Resource sheets and activity sheets

Read and discuss 'Top secret!' as a class. This could lead to a discussion on the ways in which it is necessary to keep certain information secret today; for example, encryption to prevent Internet fraud.

'Deciphering the code' provides students with an opportunity to decipher and use a simple code using a code key so that they understand the concept behind code breaking. (Answers: message 1 – The plane is arriving tomorrow; message 2 – John Smith is a spy do not trust him.)

'Enigma' tells the story of how the Nazi codes were finally broken.

'Wanted: code-breakers' can be used to consolidate the importance of the work at Bletchley Park. It encourages students to consider the skills and qualities necessary to perform such a vitally important wartime job.

'Could you be a Bletchley boffin?' gives students the opportunity to create and use their own secret code.

### Plenary

Invite students to explain to the class how their own secret code works or allow students to write a word in their secret code for the whole class to try to decipher.

# Top secret!

During the war, it was very important that some information was kept **top secret**. This was because if the enemy knew what you were planning to do before you actually did it, they would be able to find a way to stop you. This was a huge problem because sometimes it was necessary to pass on this information to other people who were on the same side but who were a long distance away. For example, a British war ship in the middle of the ocean would need to be able to contact Great Britain in order to receive its orders.

One solution to this problem was **Morse code**. This changed letters and numbers into a series of beeping sounds that could be sent out as a **radio signal**. The **Morse code operators** had to translate a message into Morse code and tap it into a special machine that sent the information out. Another Morse code operator at the other end would have to **decipher** the code by listening to the sounds and translating them into letters and words.

However, as it was sent over the radio, anybody would be able to listen in. This meant that the information could not be kept a secret. To stop this from happening, people began to use **codes**. This means that the messages would have the letters jumbled up so that they would not make sense to anybody who was listening in who should not have been. Only the people who were on your side would know how to **decipher the code**.

# Deciphering the code

☞ Look closely at the following code key. Use this code to decipher the following messages.

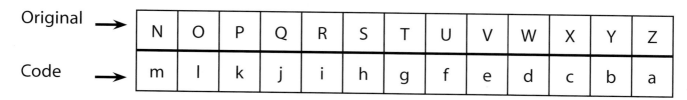

Original →

| A | B | C | D | E | F | G | H | I | J | K | L | M |
|---|---|---|---|---|---|---|---|---|---|---|---|---|
| z | y | x | w | v | u | t | s | r | q | p | o | n |

Code →

Original →

| N | O | P | Q | R | S | T | U | V | W | X | Y | Z |
|---|---|---|---|---|---|---|---|---|---|---|---|---|
| m | l | k | j | i | h | g | f | e | d | c | b | a |

Code →

Message 1:

gsv kozmv rh ziirermt glnliild

_____

_____

Message 2:

qlsm hnrgs rh z hkb wl mlg gifhg srn

_____

_____

☞ Use the code key to create your own secret message below.

_____

_____

_____

☞ Swap your message with a partner to see if you can decipher each other's message.

_____

_____

_____

World War 2

# Enigma

At the beginning of the war, the Nazis came up with a brilliant new machine that could translate a message into code. The code would change every day. This meant that it was impossible for their enemies to decipher the secret messages that they sent. The machine was called the **Enigma** and it looked very much like a typewriter.

### The boffins at Bletchley Park

The British government worked very hard to crack the Enigma codes. This was a very difficult job because the Enigma machines could translate messages into millions of different code combinations. Unless you had a key to the code, it could take several months to crack it.

The government set up a special secret code-breaking department at Bletchley Park. They recruited thousands of the most intelligent people from all over the country to work there. However, despite all their hard work, they still could not crack the Enigma code. What they needed was an Enigma machine and the top-secret code-book that went with it.

The boffins got what they needed in May 1941 when the Royal Navy found a machine and the code-books on a sinking **U-boat**. The British kept their discovery a secret, as they did not want the Nazis to stop using the Enigma machine.

The code-breakers at Bletchley Park, Buckinghamshire helped Britain and its allies to win the war as they warned them of the Nazis' plans in advance. For example, before the D-Day landings, the allies already knew where the Nazi soldiers would be and how many of them there were. This meant that they could surprise the Nazis.

World War 2

# Wanted: code-breakers

To be a code-breaker, you had to be a very special type of person. Code-breakers had to be very good at mathematics or be excellent at solving problems. They had to work for very long hours, often overnight as Bletchley Park worked 24 hours a day, seven days a week. The work they did was very repetitive and could be very boring, but the code-breakers had to concentrate very hard to decipher the thousands of coded messages that came in to Bletchley Park every week. Added to all of this, most of the coded messages were in German or other foreign languages, so the code-breakers had to be **bilingual** in order to understand them! The work was also **classified**, so everybody who worked at Bletchley Park had to know how to keep a secret!

☞ You have been asked to recruit new code-breakers for Bletchley Park. Complete the following newspaper advertisement for the job. Remember to include the skills that a code-breaker must have as well as the type of job that they will have to do. But remember – Bletchley Park is top secret, so you cannot advertise that the job is cracking codes for the government!

---

### *Staff wanted for large stately home*

---

# Could you be a Bletchley boffin?

☞ You have been asked by the government to create a code for the British to use. You can use letters, numbers or symbols in your code, but you must use a different one for each letter of the alphabet. Put your code on the typewriter keyboard below.

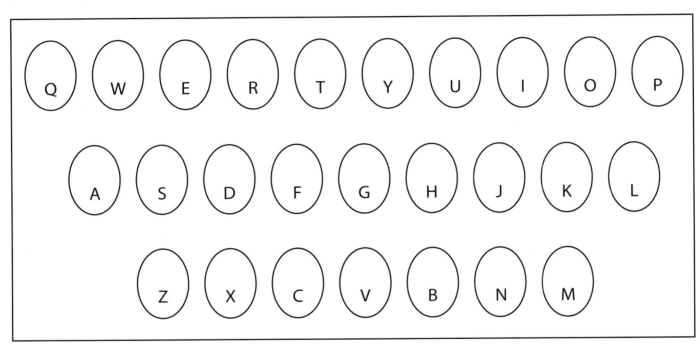

☞ Translate the top-secret message below into your code. Write it in the boxes provided.

The

Nazis

are

planning

to

invade

Britain.

We

need

to

bring

the

Normandy

plans

forward

a

week.

# Teacher's notes

## How did the government use propaganda?

### Objectives

- Understand that propaganda was used to gain public support
- Investigate the different types of propaganda used
- Develop source skills

### Prior knowledge

Students should have an understanding of how the war affected everyday life at home. They need to have completed 'What was life like at home?'

### QCA link

Unit 18 Twentieth-century conflicts

### NC links

History skills 2c, 3a, 3b, 4a, 4b

### Scottish attainment targets

Environmental Studies – Technology – People in the Past
Strand – Nature of historical evidence
Level D
Strand – People, events and societies of significance in the past
Level E

### Northern Ireland NC links

Study unit 4, The Twentieth Century World
a) the impact of World War

## Background

Propaganda was not a new concept for the British government during World War 2. It had been used extensively and successfully during World War 1. During World War 2, some of the propaganda used became subtler than it had been before. However, most British families had a radio during this time, and the cinema was a very popular form of entertainment, so the propaganda used in World War 2 could be spread through a variety of different mediums. Propaganda films were churned out throughout the war. Each had a clear message for the British public

that encouraged them to hate the Nazis and do their duty. Also, government departments, such as the Ministry of Food, used propaganda to help alleviate the pressure of rationing.

### Starter activity

Ask students to each write down the advertising slogan that they remember the most. Discuss as a class why we remember particular adverts. How do the advertisers get their message across?

### Resource sheets and activity sheets

Read and discuss 'Persuading the public' as a class. Ensure that students understand what is meant by the term 'propaganda'. Discuss ways in which the government try to get their message across today. Does propaganda still exist? Do they believe that propaganda was necessary during World War 2?

'Propaganda for a purpose' gives the students an opportunity to investigate a primary source from the time. Students should examine the source carefully in order to identify the propaganda message in the picture. It may be helpful to point out the faces on the wall in the picture. Who are they? What do they represent?

'Pots and pans for planes' gives students the opportunity to look at propaganda from the government's perspective as they create a piece of original propaganda. The students need to convince the public to donate metal to make aeroplanes and make them feel good about it.

'The power of one' examines the way in which Churchill used his speeches as a way of delivering a propaganda message. This could be extended by allowing students to read or listen to some of Churchill's most famous speeches to see how he got his message across.

In 'Could you be one of Churchill's speechwriters?', students are given the opportunity to write a rousing speech for Churchill.

### Plenary

Hot seat one or two of the more outgoing students to read their speeches to the class in the style of Churchill, or read out a selection of them yourself. Then have the students ask them questions.

# Persuading the public

The general public can be a very difficult group to convince. Many people do not like being told what to do or do not like change. However, it is the government's job to do both these things. The trick is to make these changes or orders sound like a good idea, then the public will do as they are told quite happily. It is a bit like **advertising**. If a company wants you to buy their product, it advertises it to make it seem appealing. Think about all the posters or commercials you see every day. They give you reasons why you should use that product. Advertising is a very successful idea. We can all be convinced by a good **advert**.

The government also use a form of advertising. Using a wide variety of different methods, the government can convince the public to do what they want, or more importantly, to think a certain way. This is called **propaganda**. During World War 2, the British government were very good at propaganda. It was very important that the public supported the government and the war effort.

Wartime propaganda took many forms. Sometimes it was used to encourage people to do things to help the war effort, such as the **Dig for Victory** campaign. Propaganda was used in films and books to encourage people to hate the Nazis and support the war. Often, the government would use propaganda as a way of boosting **morale**. This was very important because the war dragged on for many years and the public had to suffer hardships such as **rationing** or the **Blitz**. The government did not want to lose the support of the public during such difficult times.

British Lion films present......

OUR HEROES

Watch our heroes as they show Hitler what REAL men are made of!

World War 2

# Propaganda for a purpose

☞ Some government propaganda carried a very serious message during the war. Look closely at the poster below. What is it trying to say to the public? Write you answer on the lines provided below.

This poster is saying that _____

_____

_____

_____

# Pots and pans for planes

Imagine that you work for the government creating propaganda campaigns. It is 1940 and Great Britain is in the middle of the Blitz. The public are getting tired of being constantly bombed and they feel powerless to stop it. Your job is to raise morale. The government has come up with a story that will make the public feel that they are doing something worthwhile to stop the bombing. They have decided to tell them that they want the public to donate all their spare pots and pans so that they can make more planes to beat the Nazis. Of course, you know that this is not true because planes need to be made out of good quality metal, but you understand that the public need to feel like they are doing something to help.

☞ Design a poster to convince the public that the government needs pots and pans to build more planes. You can use a separate piece of paper or the template below.

---

## An urgent message from the government:

### *WE NEED YOUR HELP NOW!*

---

# The power of one

In 1940, the war was at its worst for Great Britain. Hitler's **Blitzkreig** was bombarding the country from the air and the war was not going well for British soldiers in Europe. Hitler and the Nazis appeared to be winning and the biggest fear for those people left at home was that Britain was under serious threat of **invasion**.

In this year, Winston Churchill became Prime Minster of Great Britain. He had a huge task on his hands. Not only did he have to turn Britain's fortunes in the war, but he also needed to raise the morale of the country.

Churchill understood that the nation was looking to its leaders to give them hope that they could still win the war. As television and the Internet were not available in 1940, everybody relied on radio to tell them what was going on. Churchill used this to great effect by giving inspiring speeches to the nation. Whenever he spoke in this way, the whole country gathered around their radios to listen to what he had to say. Many of these speeches were so inspirational that they are still famous today.

**Some of Churchill's most famous words:**

'The Battle of Britain is about to begin … If we can stand up to him, all Europe may be free … But if we fail, then the whole world … will sink into the abyss of a new Dark Age … Let us therefore brace ourselves to our duties, and so … men will still say, "This was their finest hour".' 18 June 1940.

# Could you be one of Churchill's speechwriters?

Winston Churchill was an excellent **orator**. This means that he was very good at public speaking. He was also very good at coming up with ideas for speeches, but he was a very busy man who did not have the time to write them all. He had a team of talented **speechwriters** who worked for him. These writers made sure that the speeches made by the Prime Minister were inspiring and boosted the morale of the public. In fact, many of these speeches were **propaganda** as well.

☞ You have been asked to write one of Churchill's speeches during the Blitz. Write a speech on the template below that will raise the morale of the people of London who are being bombed.

People of London, _____

_____

_____

_____

_____

_____

_____

_____

_____

_____

_____

_____

_____

World War 2

# Teacher's notes

## Who were the heroes of World War 2?

### Objectives

- Learn about individuals in World War 2
- Independently research for information
- Be able to recall, select and organise information
- Communicate knowledge using ICT

### Prior knowledge

Students should have some basic understanding of World War 2 and know that Britain and her allies were fighting the Nazis.

### QCA link

*Unit 18* Twentieth-century conflicts

### NC links

History skills 2e, 4a, 4b, 5a, 5c7a

### Scottish attainment targets

*Environmental Studies – Social Subjects – People in the Past*
Strand – People, events and societies of significance in the past
Level E
*Environmental Studies – Social Subjects – People in the Past*
Strand – Nature of historical evidence
Level E
*Environmental Studies – Skills in Social Subjects – Enquiry*
Strand – Carrying out tasks
Level E

### Northern Ireland NC links

Study unit 4, The Twentieth Century World
a) the impact of World War

## Background

It is very easy when studying such a large topic as World War 2 to forget that, for everyone concerned, the war was a very personal matter. Undeniably, the war had global implications, but it is the story of individuals that is often more inspiring and amazing, and therefore more engaging to students. The four individuals explored in this unit each, in their own way, showed tremendous tenacity, selflessness and bravery in their quest to serve their country. Their stories, although unique, provide only a small snapshot of the type of heroism that was displayed during the war by countless others.

### Starter activity

Discuss with the class the following question: What type of person is a hero? Record their ideas on a spider diagram on the board.

### Resource sheets and activity sheet

This unit is designed to encourage students to research and learn independently using the resource sheets and the Internet. Students will require a separate research sheet for each individual that they study. On the research sheet, they can record any information they find out, both from the resource sheets and the Internet.

The materials can be used in two ways. First, the resource sheets 'Who needs legs? The story of Douglas Bader', 'Just doing her duty! The story of Violette Szabo', 'Dambuster! The story of Guy Gibson' and 'Lying to stay alive! The story of Odette Sansom' can be used to provide a brief insight into the lives of the four individuals. Students should initially read one of the resource sheets and then fill in the activity sheet 'Research sheet' for that person. This option gives students an interesting overview and a chance to use the Internet for independent research.

The second option expands upon these tasks. Using their initial research as a basis, students should select one of the individuals to focus on. Using the resource sheet, their own research and other media, if available, they could create a computer slide presentation on the life and achievements of this individual. This provides an excellent assessment opportunity, gives students the chance to work independently and incorporates ICT into their studies.

### Plenary

Ask for volunteers to explain what is the most inspiring thing they have learned today.

# Who needs legs? The story of Douglas Bader

Douglas Bader joined the **Royal Air Force** in 1930 and trained to be a pilot. He proved to be an excellent pilot, but he could be very arrogant and often did things that were against the rules. One day, Bader was encouraged by some men to perform **acrobatic stunts** in his plane. It went horribly wrong and he crashed his plane. Douglas nearly died and his injuries were so bad that the doctors had to **amputate** both his legs. He was only 21 years old. The doctors told him that he would never be able to walk again. It seemed that his career as a pilot was over.

Douglas was very stubborn and proved the doctors wrong. He was given false legs made of tin, and although it was very painful, he did learn to walk on them. When war broke out in 1939, Douglas pestered the **RAF** to let him fly again. They kept refusing him. But Douglas kept trying, arguing that a pilot did not actually need legs to fly a plane. Eventually they let him back.

So far the story of Douglas Bader is pretty amazing, but Douglas knew he could do better. He believed that the RAF would do a better job if they attacked the German planes before they reached Great Britain. The RAF chose him to lead the '**Big Wing**'. This was where lots of aircraft flew in **formation** and searched for enemy planes over the English Channel. It was a huge success. One day Douglas was **shot down** over France. He was placed in a **Prisoner of War Camp**. The Germans had to take his tin legs away because he tried to escape so much! Finally, they sent him to a special camp called **Colditz**. The story of his life was made into a film called *Reach for the Sky*.

# Just doing her duty! The story of Violette Szabo

Violette Szabo was born in France. Her mother was French, but her father was English. Although Violette spent her early years in France, the family returned to England when she was still a child, so Violette spoke French but with an English accent.

During the war, Violette met and fell in love with a young French soldier who was visiting London. Very quickly they got married and had a daughter. Violette's husband had to go back to the war to fight and was killed shortly afterwards. Violette received the bad news in a **telegram** and vowed to avenge his death by working against the Nazis. She joined the **Special Operations Executive** to train as a secret agent. However, she was not a very good student and many of her superiors had doubts about how suitable she was for the job.

Despite this, Violette was sent to France where she worked with the **French Resistance**. After completing some very successful missions, Violette and a man called Jacques Dufour, who was a member of the French Resistance, were ambushed by some Nazi soldiers. Violette was an expert with a gun and her brave actions allowed Dufour to escape, but she was not so lucky. She was captured by the **Gestapo** and had to endure terrible **torture** for many weeks. Violette did not tell the Gestapo anything so they sent her to a **concentration camp** and sentenced her to death.

Violette was executed by a **firing squad** at the concentration camp. She was only 23 years old. After she died, she was awarded the **George Cross** medal. This is the highest award for bravery that a civilian can receive. Her award was collected by her four-year-old daughter. The story of Violette Szabo's life was made into a film called *Carve Her Name With Pride*.

# Dambuster! The story of Guy Gibson

Guy Gibson joined the **Royal Air Force** just before the war started and trained as a pilot. In the early part of the war, Guy proved himself to be an excellent pilot. Eventually the RAF promoted Guy to the rank of **Wing Commander** and put him in charge of **617 Squadron**. He was only 23 years old!

The Nazis relied on a place called the **Ruhr Valley** to keep them supplied with the raw materials to make airplanes, tanks and weapons. This was a huge **industrial** area in Germany where there were many mines and factories. The British realised that if they could destroy some of the enormous **dams** in the area, then the damage to the industrial areas would take years for the Nazis to repair.

The big problem with this plan was that the Nazis also knew that the Ruhr was too important to allow it to be attacked, so it was heavily protected by soldiers, planes and **anti-aircraft guns**. Also, traditional bombs were not very effective on the dams, so Guy and 617 Squadron practised using a new **bouncing bomb** that had just been developed.

In May 1943, Guy led the **Dambusters** on their mission. The mission was extremely dangerous as the planes had to fly very low through the anti-aircraft fire in order to hit the dams that were their target. After many failed attempts, the dams finally collapsed and the Ruhr was flooded with water. Guy was awarded the **Victoria Cross** for his bravery that night. The story of how the dams were destroyed was made into a film called *The Dambusters*.

# Lying to stay alive! The story of Odette Sansom

Odette Sansom was born in France in 1912, but she married a British man and moved to England with him. They had three daughters and Odette was happy as a housewife. However, when the war broke out and her home country of France fell to the Nazis, Odette wanted to do something more to help.

As Odette could speak French, the **Special Operations Executive (SOE)**, a secret organisation that placed spies in enemy **occupied** countries, recruited her to work for them.

Odette was smuggled into France in 1942 and was sent to work with **SOE operative** Peter Churchill. Their job was to work with the **French Resistance** to spy on the Nazis. For many months, they were able to continue this work in secret. However, one day they were betrayed to the Nazis by a **double agent**.

Odette and Peter Churchill were taken prisoner by the **Gestapo**. These were the most feared Nazi soldiers who were famous for being cruel and for torturing their prisoners. Odette knew many secrets and she knew that it would be very dangerous for other **SOE operatives** if she talked. Odette was violently tortured. All her toenails and fingernails were pulled out by the roots, but she never betrayed her friends. Instead, she convinced the Nazis that Peter Churchill was the nephew of the British Prime Minister Winston Churchill, and that she was Peter's wife! This lie probably saved both their lives, as although Odette was sentenced to death and sent to a **concentration camp**, the Nazis were reluctant to kill her because they believed she had links to the British government. Odette was freed when the war ended and married Peter Churchill, as her first husband had died. The story of her life was made into a film called *Odette*.

World War 2

# Activity sheet – Who were the heroes of World War 2?

# Research sheet for:_____

☞ Use both the resource sheet and the Internet to find information about the hero you are studying. Use this sheet to record any information that you have found.

Date of birth     _____     Marital status     _____

Date of death     _____     Children     _____

Job before the war     _____

_____

Job during the war     _____

_____

Medals and honours     _____

_____

During my research, I found out the following information about this person:

1 _____

2 _____

3 _____

4 _____

5 _____

6 _____

7 _____

8 _____

9 _____

10 _____

# Teacher's notes

## How did the war end?

### Objectives

- Understand the war ended in Europe
- Investigate the reasons why the atomic bomb was dropped on Japan
- Define all the keywords

### Prior knowledge

Students should know that World War 2 went on for five years and that there were many significant phases and battles during the war.

### QCA link

*Unit 18* Twentieth-century conflicts

### NC links

History skills 3a, 3b, 5c, 7a, 7b, 7d

### Scottish attainment targets

Strand – Change and continuity, cause and effect
Level E
*Environmental Studies – Social Subjects – People in the Past*
Strand – Nature of historical evidence
Level E
*Environmental Studies – Social Subjects - Developing Informed Attitudes*
Strand – Social and environmental responsibility
Level E

### Northern Ireland NC links

Study unit 4, The Twentieth Century World
a) the impact of World War, a major event, e.g. the dropping of the atomic bomb 1945
b) a major event or person, e.g. the dropping of the atomic bomb 1945

## Background

By early 1945, it seemed inevitable that the Nazis would lose the war. They had lost considerable ground from 1944 onwards and Hitler no longer had the unconditional support from his officers and colleagues. Many high-ranking Nazis began to question his leadership and tactics and at least one plot to kill the Führer was uncovered. As Hitler's mental state declined, the allies continued their furious march towards Berlin.

Meanwhile, in the Pacific, the Japanese showed no signs of giving up willingly, despite the best efforts of the allies against them. As the situation for Japan became more desperate, the Japanese tactics became more extreme. The use of Kamikaze pilots, and other types of suicide missions made the United States increasingly uneasy about their enemy and they were eager to see an end to the whole war as soon as possible.

### Starter activity

Divide the students into small groups and give each group a large piece of paper and some colouring pens. Each group should use these to create a mind map that shows what they have learned about World War 2 so far.

### Resource sheets and activity sheets

Read and discuss 'Suicide and surrender' as a class. Students may benefit from scanning the timelines of World War 2 that they created earlier in the topic.

In groups, students should use 'And now for the news…' to create radio speeches about the end of the war using the template provided. The finished scripts could then be performed or recorded.

'Enola Gay' provides information about the decision to use the atomic bomb against Japan to end the war. This can be used for a decision-making activity or a debate using 'The verdict'.

'The verdict' presents the students with some of the arguments for and against the use of the first nuclear bomb.

'Keyword snap (1)' and '(2)' can be used in different ways. It could be used as a keyword and definition card sorting activity. Alternatively, it could be used as a game of 'snap'. Photocopy the keyword cards on a different coloured piece of paper to the definition cards. Cut out each deck of cards and give one each to two students. They then play snap in the traditional way, except that to get a pair in this version, students need to match the correct keyword to its corresponding definition.

### Plenary

Engage the students in a quick game of keyword hangman.

# Suicide and surrender

After the success of the **D-Day** landings in June 1944, the war changed. Hitler and the Nazis no longer seemed to be winning and the combined forces of Britain, the United States and the Soviet Union, along with their allies, were able to push the Nazis back towards Germany. One by one, the countries that had been invaded by Hitler were now being **liberated**. By 1945, it was becoming obvious that Hitler was losing the war.

In April 1945, the allied troops had surrounded Germany and were beginning to march towards the capital city of Berlin. It appears that Hitler could not cope with the idea that his plans for a **Third Reich** had failed. On 30 April 1945, he committed suicide in an underground bunker in Berlin. There are many theories about what actually happened and as the body was burned afterwards, we will never know for sure how Hitler died. However, the most common theory is that he shot himself and his girlfriend, Eva Braun, because he could not accept defeat.

Shortly after Hitler's death, on 7 May 1945, Germany **surrendered**. After six long years, the war in Europe was finally over. The people of Britain celebrated with a huge party. On the 8 May 1945, the streets were filled with people singing and dancing. They called this day VE Day. (VE is short for Victory in Europe!)

# And now for the news…

☞ Most people in 1945 listened to the radio to find out what was going on in the war. Imagine you are a radio broadcaster in 1945. It is your job to tell the people of Britain that the war has ended. Use the template below to write your news script about Hitler's death and Germany's surrender.

And now for the news on 7 May 1945

# Enola Gay

Even though the war in Europe was now over, the war in the Pacific was still going on. Japan was still fighting despite Germany's surrender. The United States wanted the war to end as soon as possible and became frustrated with the situation with Japan. The President of the United States, Harry S. Truman, warned the Japanese that he would send all his armed forces to Japan and invade the country unless they stopped fighting. The Japanese ignored this threat. Truman had to do something.

At around this time, a new type of bomb had been developed. It was called the **atom bomb** and it was the first **nuclear** bomb. The atom bomb was very powerful and was capable of destroying whole cities. The United States made the decision to use the atom bomb against Japan. Even to this day, many people believe that this was the wrong decision.

On 6 August 1945, a plane called the **Enola Gay** was loaded with an atom bomb. It flew over the Japanese city of Hiroshima and dropped the bomb. The results were devastating. A huge part of the city was destroyed instantly and approximately 140 000 people were killed.

Unfortunately, the deaths did not end there, as there are serious side effects to a nuclear explosion. **Radiation** poisoned the land and many animals and children were born with **deformities** years after the blast. Thousands more died of cancer. After a second atomic bomb was dropped on Nagasaki a few days later, the Japanese surrendered on 14 August 1945. World War 2 was finally over.

# Activity sheet – How did the war end?

# The verdict

 To this day, people argue about whether it was right to drop the atom bomb on Japan. Below are some of the arguments for and against this. Look closely at these and discuss them with a partner. When you are sure you understand both sides of the argument, you need to make a decision. Was it right or wrong to drop the atomic bomb on Japan in 1945? Back your decision with reasons why and write them in the box below.

| Reasons for the bomb | | Reasons against the bomb | |
| --- | --- | --- | --- |
| ✓ | The war had gone on long enough. Something had to be done. | ✗ | Hundreds of thousands of innocent people were killed and many suffered later on because of the radiation. |
| ✓ | The Japanese ignored several warnings from the United States. | ✗ | Russia had just declared war on Japan. They could have helped the USA to beat Japan. |
| ✓ | The Japanese do not believe in surrender. It is against their culture. | ✗ | The United States should have made the results of testing the bomb more public to give Japan a warning. |
| ✓ | The Japanese were using new tactics. They were now using Kamikaze pilots. This means that the pilot would kill himself in order to blow something up! | ✗ | The Japanese people were starving. They could not fight for much longer. |
| ✓ | The United States and its allies would lose thousands more men if the fighting continued. | ✗ | The atom bomb had not been fully tested. Nobody knew how bad the side effects would be. |
| ✓ | Japanese attack on Pearl Harbor. | | |

In my opinion, the United States SHOULD/SHOULD NOT have dropped the atomic bomb.

I believe this because _____

_____

_____

# Keyword snap (1)

☞ Play this game with a partner. Cut out the following keyword and definition cards. One player should have the keyword cards. The other player should have the definition cards. If the keyword matches the definition card, say 'snap'.

**KEYWORD CARDS:**

| | | |
|---|---|---|
| Rationing | Blackout | Nazi |
| Propaganda | Appeasement | Home Front |
| Evacuee | Luftwaffe | Spitfire |
| Blitz | Enigma | Air raid |
| Invade | Surrender | Atom bomb |

# Keyword snap (2)

 Play this game with a partner. Cut out the following keyword and definition cards. One player should have the keyword cards. The other player should have the definition cards. If the keyword matches the definition card, say 'snap'.

**DEFINITION CARDS:**

| | | |
|---|---|---|
| Food was shared out and the government issued ration books. | As soon as it got dark, all lights had to be covered up. | A person who shares the ideas and beliefs of Hitler. |
| Information that is created to make you think a certain way. | Trying to avoid another war by giving Hitler some of what he wanted. | The things people did at home to help the war effort. |
| A child who has been sent to safety in the countryside. | The German air force. | A fast and well-designed British plane. |
| The nickname of the German air attacks on British towns and cities. | The German code-making machine. | The name given to an attack on a town or city by planes. |
| When one country takes over another country without permission. | To give up and agree to stop fighting. | A powerful nuclear bomb capable of destroying a whole city. |

# Assessment sheet – World War 2

✓ Tick the boxes that show what you know.

| I know: | Yes | Not sure | Don't know |
|---|---|---|---|
| why Hitler came to power | | | |
| what propaganda is | | | |
| how World War 2 started | | | |
| what the Home Front was | | | |
| why rationing was introduced | | | |
| what an evacuee is | | | |
| how the public protected themselves in an air raid | | | |
| why the government used codes | | | |
| what an Enigma machine is | | | |
| how the war ended | | | |
| how to research using the Internet | | | |
| how to spell the keywords | | | |

One thing that I found most interesting about this topic is:

_____

_____

I would like to learn more about:

_____

_____

_____